DIAMONDS

DIAMONDS

*This book is designed to assist you in acquiring a basic knowledge
of the diamond industry and to deepen your understanding of the main factors
which determine the value and quality of a diamond.*

By Marijan Dundek, IGI

*I would like to express my gratitude to De Beers
for their special assistance and help
in the realization of this project*

Published in 1999 by
NOBLE GEMS PUBLICATIONS

Copyright © Marijan Dundek 1999
Pages 8, 9 & 23 by the courtesy of © De Beers
Pages 15, 16 & 31 of © Lazare Kaplan

Art consultant Tala Shaker

Designed and produced by
BBB Design Group PLC, London

A CIP catalogue record for this book is available from the British Library

ISBN 0 9535371 1 0 – 2nd revised edition
(ISBN 0 9535371 0 2 – 1st edition)

Printed in UK by Redwood Books, Trowbridge, Wiltshire.

NOBLE GEMS PUBLICATIONS
3 Olaf Court, 50a, Kensington Church Street, London, W8 4DG. UK.
Tel: 44-20 7938 3682 Fax: 44-20 7937 8251

Contents

PROPERTIES OF DIAMONDS

Chemical composition: C, Crystallized carbon
Crystal system: Isometric (cubic)
Mohs' hardness: 10
Specific gravity: 3.417 – 3.55

Refractive index: 2.417–2.419
Transparency: Transparent
Dispersion: 0.044

Diamonds are the most cherished and highly valued of gemstones. Throughout history, they have been admired by Kings and worn as a symbol of strength, courage and invincibility. Over the centuries the diamond acquired unique status as the ultimate gift of love, in myth and reality. The word 'diamond' comes from the Greek *adamas*, meaning unconquerable. It is the hardest mineral known to man, yet it has the simplest chemical composition being crystalized carbon.

DIAMOND GENESIS

The exact origin of diamonds is still something of a mystery even today. It is known that diamonds were created by Nature more than 3 billion years ago. The elemental forces of heat and pressure miraculously transformed carbon into diamonds deep below the surface of the earth. The volcanic mass in which this crystallization took place then thrust upwards, broke through the earth's surface to cool in kimberlite or lamproite pipes where most diamonds are found today. It is not an easy task to recover gem-quality and industrial diamonds and approximately 250 tonnes of ore must be mined and processed from the average kimberlite pipe to produce a one carat polished gem-quality diamond. Thus, it is easy to understand why diamonds are so rare and valuable.

To transform a rough diamond it takes skilled craftsmen to unlock and reveal the fantastic beauty that lies within, with all its various colours which range from white, black through to yellow, champagne, green, blue, pink and the very rare red.

Today, diamonds are the most mined and carefully graded gems. They are cut with great precision and delicacy, and come in many shapes, quality and price. Their beauty, mystery and magic shine for millions around the world and say all that the heart feels but words cannot express.

DIAMOND-PRODUCING COUNTRIES & MAJOR CUTTING CENTRES

Diamonds were mined in India more than 2800 years ago, but the modern industry began with the discovery of diamonds in South Africa in the late 19th century. Today, De Beers is the world's largest diamond-mining company and the most important producer.

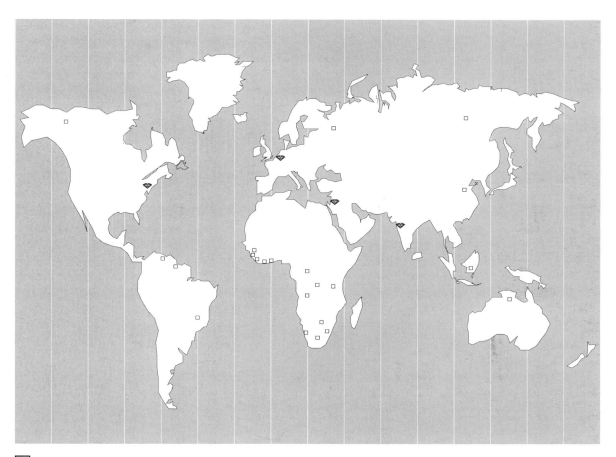

☐ MAJOR PRODUCING COUNTRIES
Australia, Angola, Zaire, Botswana, Russia, South Africa and Namibia

OTHER PRODUCINC COUNTRIES

Brazil, Canada, Guyana, Venezuela, Guinea, Sierra Leone, Liberia, Ivory Coast, Ghana, Central African Republic, Tanzania, China, and Indonesia .

◈ MAJOR CUTTING CENTRES
Antwerp, Bombay, New York and Tel Aviv.

OTHER COUNTRIES WHERE DIAMONDS ARE CUT

Australia	Great Britain	Mauritius	South Africa
Botswana	Haiti	Netherlands	South Korea
Brazil	Hong Kong	North Korea	Sri Lanka
China	Indonesia	Philippines	Taiwan
Dominican	Japan	Portugal	Tanzania
Republic	Malaysia	Puerto Rico	Thailand
Germany	Malta	Russia	Tunisia
			Vietnam

DE BEERS AND THE DIAMOND INDUSTRY

DE BEERS AND DIAMONDS

For over 100 years, De Beers has been involved in all aspects of the diamond business. In each of these categories, it possesses unrivaled mining and recovery expertise. It is also active in every type of diamond mining: from open cast, underground, alluvial, coastal to undersea.

Today, De Beers is the largest diamond mining company in the world, producing around 40 percent of the world's gem diamonds by value from its mines in South Africa, and in partnership with government, in Botswana and Namibia. De Beers also expects to start mining diamonds in Canada from 2006. Its support for the diamond industry brings significant benefits to every diamond producing nation.

Most rough diamonds from the major producing nations come to London where the Diamond Trading Company (DTC), the Sales & Marketing arm of De Beers, sorts, values and sells about 50 percent of the world's annual production.

The DTC undertakes the advertising and promotion of diamond jewellery on behalf of the industry – spending $200 million around the world annually in close co–operation with our clients and the jewellery trade.

De Beers is a truly international company with offices and associates in many countries including the UK, Israel, Belgium, Russia, Hong Kong, India, Botswana, Namibia, Angola, Canada, Australia, Japan, South Africa and Tanzania.

SORTING AND VALUING

Fifty percent of the world's rough diamonds come to the London offices of the DTC. Here they are sorted into more than 14 000 categories of shape, quality, colour and size. This complex process, involving millions of carats, is carried out by several hundred highly–trained sorters as well as modern automated machines and computerised control system (many of which are designed and build by the DTC's own research and development laboratories). These are essential on making the task of sorting such large volumes of diamonds possible.

A master sample is used to guarantee that sorting is carried out consistently. Diamond sorting also takes place in Gaborone, Windhoek and Kimberley.

To ensure that identical standards operate throughout the world, official producer and working samples are used by representatives from the producing nation – usually government appointed valuators – for sorting operations in Botswana, Namibia, South Africa or London.

Official producer samples are kept under the joint seals of both producer and the DTC. Additional safeguards involve the use of laser techniques to etch a reference number into the surface of each stone in the master samples.

SALES AND MARKETING

Once sorted, diamonds are blended into "selling mixtures" in preparation for sale to the DTC's clients, or sight holders as they are also known, comprising around 80 of the most experienced diamond manufactures and dealers in the world.

Most of these sight holders are based in the traditional diamond centres of Antwerp, Tel Aviv, Mumbai, New York and Johannesburg. Sales or "Sights" take place ten times a year in London and Johannesburg. Sight holders have the advantage of knowing that the DTC will attempt to provide diamonds of right size, quality to match specific requirements, within the confines of its own availability.

In response to the changing business environment in the diamond industry, the DTC is transforming the way it does business with its clients. This initiative is called Supplier of Choice, and heralds a more marketing–orientated approach. Through services provided by the DTC, it can equip sight holders that have been selected using objective criteria, to identify opportunities in the market place and distribute their diamonds more efficiently into them.

Through the DTC's Diamond Promotion Service (DPS) and its Diamond Information Centres (DICs), located in all the major consumer markets around the world, the company is also able to focus on the retailer and point of sale. An international training initiative educates jewellers in how to market and sell diamonds, increase their diamond knowledge and, through the DIC's activities in promotional and media events, keep diamonds in the public eye.

The Diamond Trading Company also promotes innovation in jewellery design by organizing competitions amongst the world's leading designers, such as the Shining Light event in South Africa.

DIAMOND VALUE

There are four main factors by which the value and quality of a diamond is determined (popularly called the 4C's), and any combination of these factors will make it possible to understand the quality and the value of a gem.

These factors are: COLOUR, CLARITY, CUT and CARAT

COLOUR

Colour is the most important characteristic of a gemstone and it is one of the key factors to be considered when determining the value of a diamond. The ideal colour is the total absence of all body colour (*colourless*) except in fancy colours of yellow, pink, blue, green, champagne, black and the very rare red, where an intensive hue is an asset. A very precise scale of colour grading is in general use today in the diamond trade as defined by the GIA (*Gemmological Institute of America*). The grades are distinguished by letters of the alphabet, beginning with the letter D.

In addition to the GIA Colour Grading Scales, there are a number of other classification systems illustrated here. These are:

AGS. – American Gemological Society

SCAN. D.N. – Scandinavian Nomenclature applied in Denmark, Finland, Norway and Sweden.

CIBJO. – An International Association of the Jewellery, Silver, Pearl and Stone Trade, the *Confederation Internationale de la Bijouterie, Joaillerie, Oefevrerie, des Diamands, Perles et Pierres* founded in 1961 and which today is an association of 19 countries which include: Austria, Belgium, Canada, Denmark, Finland, France, Italy, Japan, Netherlands, Norway, Spain, Sweden, Switzerland, United Kingdom, United States and West Germany.

HRD. – Belgian *Hoge Raad voor Diamant* known as the Diamond High Council.

COLOUR GRADING SYSTEMS

AGS	GIA	SCAN D.N. UNDER 0.50 CARAT	SCAN D.N. 0.50 CARAT AND OVER	CIBJO UNDER 0.47 CARAT	CIBJO 0.50 CARAT AND OVER	HRD
0	D	White	River	Exceptional white	Exceptional white (+)	Exceptional white (+)
0	E	White	River	Exceptional white	Exceptional white	Exceptional white
1	F	White	Top wesselton	Rare white	Rare white (+)	Rare white (+)
2	G	White	Top wesselton	Rare white	Rare white	Rare white
3	H	White	Wesselton	White	White	White
4	I	Slightly tinted white	Top crystal	Slightly tinted white	Slightly tinted white (I)	Slightly tinted white
	J	Slightly tinted white	Crystal	Slightly tinted white	Slightly tinted white (J)	Slightly tinted white
5	K	Slightly tinted white	Top cape	Tinted white	Tinted white (K)	Tinted white
6	L	Slightly tinted white	Top cape	Tinted white	Tinted white (L)	Tinted white
	M	Tinted colour	Cape	Tinted colour	Tinted colour	Tinted colour
7	N	Tinted colour	Cape	Tinted colour	Tinted colour	Tinted colour
	O	Tinted colour	Light yellow	Tinted colour	Tinted colour	Tinted colour
8	P	Tinted colour	Light yellow	Tinted colour	Tinted colour	Tinted colour
	Q	Tinted colour	Light yellow	Tinted colour	Tinted colour	Tinted colour
	R	Tinted colour	Light yellow	Tinted colour	Tinted colour	Tinted colour
9-10	S-X -Z	Tinted colour	Yellow	Tinted colour	Tinted colour	Tinted colour

CLARITY (*degree of flawlessness*)

The clarity of a gemstone is assessed by examination of imperfections, inclusions *(internal objects)* and blemishes *(external marks)* under magnification of x10. Almost all diamonds contain minute traces of non-crystalized carbon or small non-diamond crystals, and are Nature's fingerprint making every diamond unique. Most of them are not visible to the naked eye and require magnification to be apparent. However, the fewer there are, the rarer the gemstone will be.

GIA CLARITY GRADING SCALE

	VVS_1 VVS_2 VS_1	VS_2	SI_1	SI_2	I_1	I_2	I_3
flawless							
Internally flawless					included		

FL	IF	VVS_1-VVS_2	VS_1- VS_2	SI_1 - SI_2	I_1 - I_2 -I_3
Loupe Clean (flawless)	Loupe Clean (internally flawless - minor surface blemishes)	(very, very small inclusions)	(very small inclusions)	(small inclusions)	(inclusions visible to naked eye)

DEFINITIONS OF CLARITY GRADES ACCORDING TO INTERNAL DEFECTS

IF
Loupe clean

A diamond is termed loupe clean when an expert (experienced gemologist) finds no internal defects with a x10 loupe. This means that the diamond does not contain any internal defects which are more detectable than a dot-like inclusion with a size of five microns and has satisfactory brightness.

VVS_1 VVS_2

Very, very small internal defects which can be detected by the expert with a x10 loupe only with degrees of difficulty ranging from very considerable to great. Size, position and number of the internal defects determine the distinction between VVS_1 and VVS_2.

VS_1 VS_2

Very small internal defects which can be detected by the expert with degrees of difficulty ranging from not too difficult to easy. Size, position and number of the internal defects determine the distinction between VS_1 and VS_2.

$S_1 S_2$

Small internal defects which are very easy for the expert to detect with a x10 loupe. Size, position and number of the internal defects determine the distinction between SI_1 and SI_2.

I_1

Internal defects which are difficult for the expert to detect with the naked eye in an examination through the crown.

I_2

Large and/or numerous internal defects which are easily detectable by the expert with the naked eye and which slightly diminishes brilliance.

I_3

Large and/or numerous internal defects which are very easily detectable by the expert with the naked eye and which diminishes brilliance.

CLARITY GRADING SYSTEMS

In addition to the GIA Clarity Grading Scale there are a number of other classification systems illustrated here. These are:

CIBJO. An International Association of the Jewellery, Silver, Pearls and Stone Trade.

HRD. Belgian *Hoge Raad voor Diamant* (The Diamond High Council).

SCAN D.N. Scandinavian Nomenclature.

AGS. American Gemological Society.

CIBJO UNDER 0.47 CARAT	CIBJO 0.47 CARAT AND OVER	HRD	SCAN D.N.	GIA	AGS
Loupe clean	Loupe clean	Loupe clean	FL	FL	0
			IF (Internally Flawless)	IF	1
VVS	VVS_1	VVS_1	VVS_1	VVS_1	
	VVS_2	VVS_2	VVS_2	VVS_2	2
VS	VS_1	VS_1	VS_1	VS_1	3
	VS_2	VS_2	VS_2	VS_2	4
SI	SI_1	SI	SI_1	SI_1	5
	SI_2		SI_2	SI_2	6
Piqué I	Piqué I	P_1	1st Piqué	I_1 (Imperfect)	7
					8
Piqué II	Piqué II	P_2	2nd Piqué	I_2	9
Piqué III	Piqué III	P_3	3rd Piqué	I_3	10

CUT

The cut of a diamond, its proportions and symmetry are of extraordinary importance as they have the greatest influence on the brilliance, liveliness or sparkle of a stone. This is the one factor most directly influenced by man as the other three are dictated by Nature. The polisher's skill is also important for shaping the stone. The most popular diamond shape is the round brilliant-cut. Other shapes, such as the emerald-cut, oval pear, heart, princes-cut, and marquise, are referred to as 'fancy cut'. The cut and proportion of a stone in the diamond trade is also known as its 'make' and overall quality can be described as very good, good, medium or poor 'make'.

THE FACETS OF A BRILLIANT-CUT AND TERMS
WHICH ARE APPLIED TO THE SECTIONS OF A DIAMOND

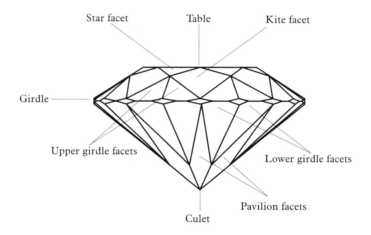

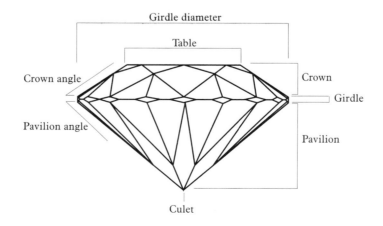

THE REFLECTIVE QUALITIES OF DIFFERENT CUTS

When a diamond is ideally cut, light rays from all sides are bent towards the centre of the stone and are reflected back through the top in a blaze of light.

When light enters a perfectly cut diamond, it is reflected from facet to facet and comes back through the top in a rainbow blaze.

If a diamond is not ideally cut, light will 'leak' out through the base or side of the diamond.

In a diamond which is cut too deep, much of the light is reflected to opposite facets at the wrong angle and is lost through the sides. The diamond may appear black in the centre.

In a diamond cut too shallow, the light 'leaks' through the bottom and the eye may see a dull reflection.

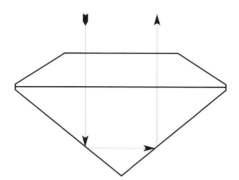

IDEAL CUT

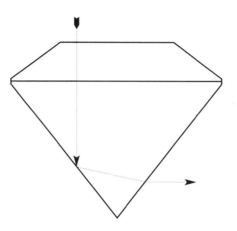

DEEP CUT

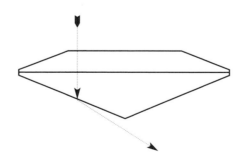

SHALLOW CUT

THE LAZARE DIAMONDS® IDEAL CUT

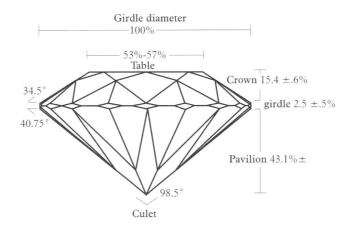

In 1919, Marcel Tolkowsky, a cousin of Lazare Kaplan, developed a mathematical formula for cutting diamonds to precise angles and proportions to gain the optimum reflection and refraction of light, creating the optimum balance, sparkle and fire to the diamond. Lazare Kaplan adopted that ideal cut theory in 1919 and today is still devoted to the art of cutting the most beautiful diamonds in the world.

Today, fewer than 1 per cent of the world's diamonds are ideal cut and LKI is the company which produces only the best. To achieve this quality, more of the original rough diamond must be sacrificed and thus these diamonds offer better value and beauty, a standard by which all other diamonds are cut.

IDEAL PROPORTIONS OF A ROUND BRILLIANT-CUT DIAMOND

Tolkowsky – Standard American Ideal Cut

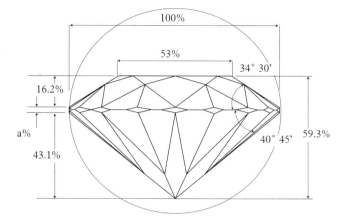

Eppler – Practical Fine Cut (*European Cut*).

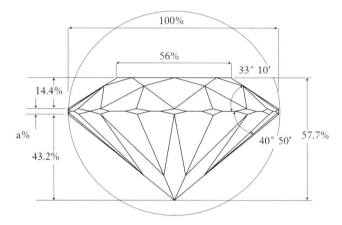

Scan D.N. – Scandinavian Standard Brilliant.

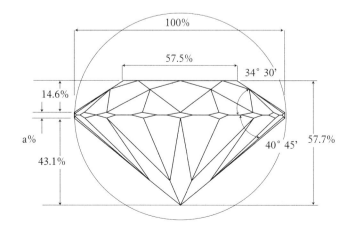

FACTORS WHICH AFFECT PROPORTIONS AND SYMMETRY

Factors which affect the proportions of a diamond are:

Table diameter
Total height of stone
Crown height
Girdle thickness and regularity
Angle of the Crown and Pavilion
Facets to the plane of the Girdle

Important features of symmetry are:

The position of the Table and Culet
The size and regularity of the Facets, Girdle and Culet

External features that affect the symmetry are:

Naturals and extra facets (*natural features*)
Twinning, growth and grain lines (*natural features*)
Fringed or rough Girdle, polishing marks, burn marks
   (*these features are caused during cutting*)
Damage (*physical damage, broken Culet, chipped Girdle, scratches*)

DIAMOND SHAPES

The shape of a diamond is governed by the way it is cut. The earliest cut gemstones were simple, restricted by the technology of the time. As techniques and tools were improved, so the cuts became more complex.

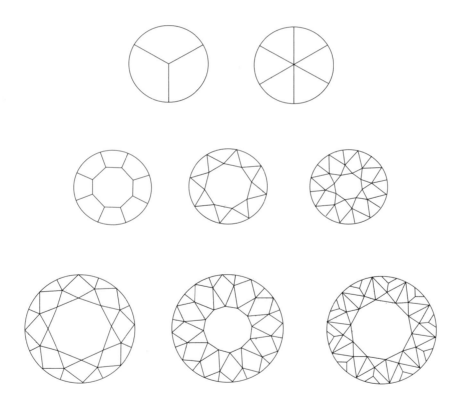

ANTIQUE FORMS OF DIAMOND CUT

This illustration shows some early 'shapes' of diamond which have been used in antique and period jewellery. Lately, these diamond shapes have grown in popularity and are undergoing a revival. People are beginning to appreciate them for their distinctive beauty, personality and romantic past.

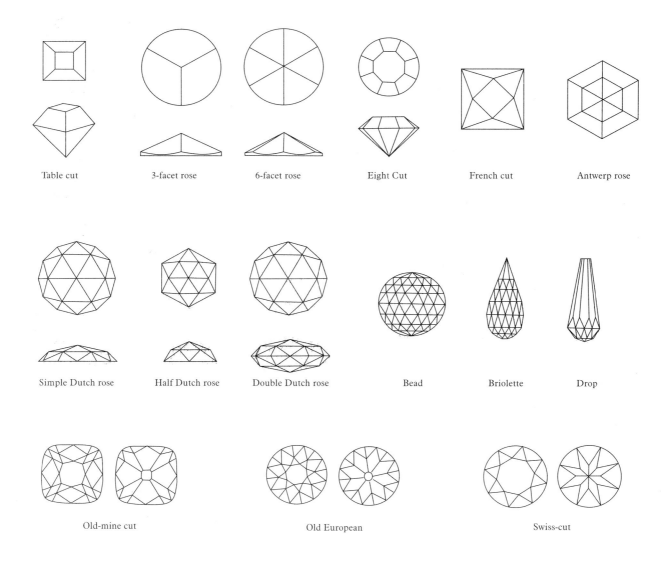

| Table cut | 3-facet rose | 6-facet rose | Eight Cut | French cut | Antwerp rose |

| Simple Dutch rose | Half Dutch rose | Double Dutch rose | Bead | Briolette | Drop |

| Old-mine cut | Old European | Swiss-cut |

CLASSIC FORMS OF DIAMOND CUT

These are the traditional shapes of a diamond generally used today. The most popular among them is the Round Brilliant-Cut Diamond with its 57 facets (but if could be counted as 58 if the culet is cut and polished). This is followed by the modified brilliant-cuts, such as Marquise, Pear, Oval and Heart-shape. In addition there are also Emerald Cut (*rectangular and square-shaped*), Baguette, Trapeze and Square Cuts.

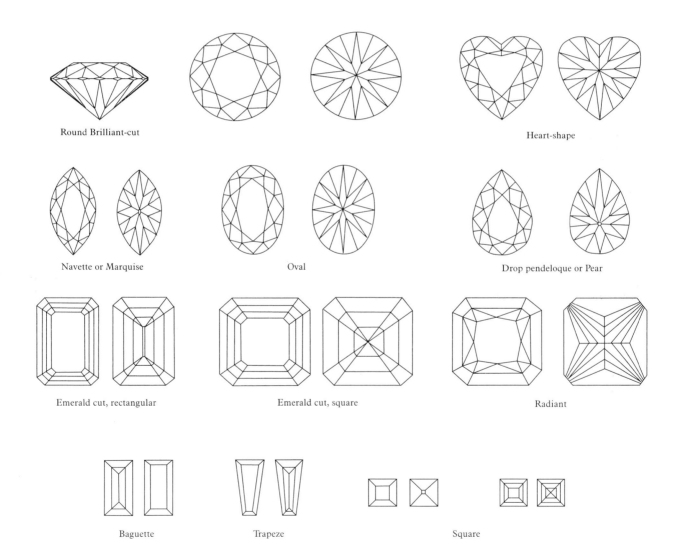

Round Brilliant-cut

Heart-shape

Navette or Marquise

Oval

Drop pendeloque or Pear

Emerald cut, rectangular

Emerald cut, square

Radiant

Baguette

Trapeze

Square

MODERN FORMS OF DIAMOND CUT

The modern shapes illustrated below are proof that human imagination has no boundaries when it comes to cutting and shaping this most treasured stone. These new shapes have created much excitement in the trade. They are very beautiful and are identified by attractive names.

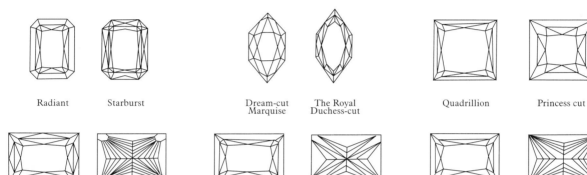

Radiant   Starburst   Dream-cut Marquise   The Royal Duchess-cut   Quadrillion   Princess cut

Some of the new Rectangular Princess cut

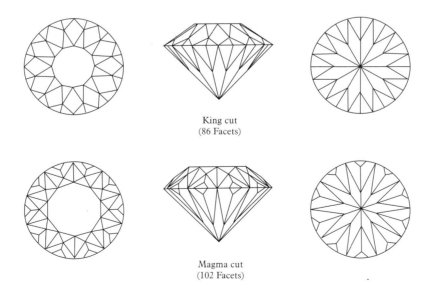

King cut
(86 Facets)

Magma cut
(102 Facets)

THE NEW FLOWER CUTS

The new flower cuts are based on unconventional angle dimensions, with large polished surfaces and the appearance of the bottom culet facing up through the top facet, creating strong brilliance and shine. The five new cuts have been named after flowers – dahlia, fire-rose, marigold, sunflower and zinnia.

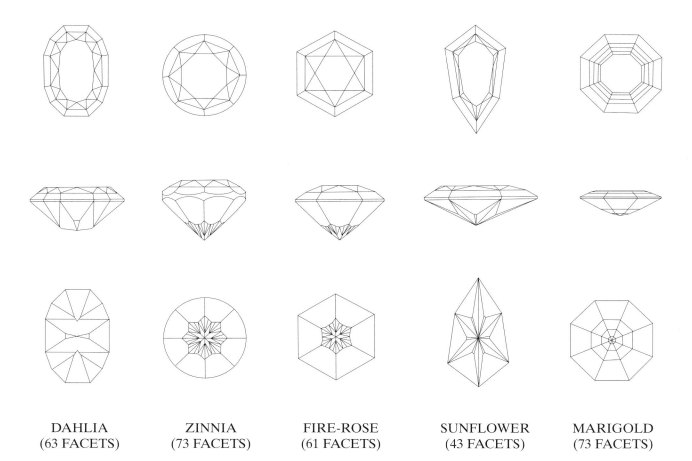

| DAHLIA | ZINNIA | FIRE-ROSE | SUNFLOWER | MARIGOLD |
| (63 FACETS) | (73 FACETS) | (61 FACETS) | (43 FACETS) | (73 FACETS) |

CARAT

The carat is a unit of weight, not size. One carat (1ct) weights 200 milligrams or ⅕ of a gram and is divided into 100 points, so that a diamond of 50 points is described as half a carat or 0.50 carats. Carat-weight (*size*) is the most obvious factor in determining the value of a diamond, but it is important to bear in mind that two stones of equal size can have very different values depending on their quality. In addition, it is important to understand that carat weight does not affect the value in diamonds proportionately, and the larger the stone, the more disproportionate the increase in cost per carat.

ROUND BRILLIANT-CUT DIAMONDS, DIAMETERS AND CORRESPONDING WEIGHTS

.03cts 2.0mm	.05cts 2.5mm	.07cts 2.7mm	.10cts 3.0mm	.15cts 3.4mm
.20cts 3.8mm	.25cts 4.1mm	.30cts 4.5mm	.40cts 4.8mm	.50cts 5.2mm
.65cts 5.6mm	.75cts 5.9mm	.85cts 6.2mm	1cts 6.5mm	1.25cts 7mm
1.50cts 7.4mm	1.75cts 7.8mm	2cts 8.2mm	2.25cts 8.6mm	2.50cts 9.0mm
3cts 9.3mm	4cts 10.2mm	5cts 11.0mm	6cts 11.7mm	7cts 12.4mm

SIZE AND WEIGHTS OF THE MOST POPULAR DIAMOND CUTS

WEIGHT (CT)	EMERALD CUT	MARQUISE CUT	PEAR SHAPE	BRILLIANT CUT
5				
4				
3				
2½				
2				
1½				
1¼				
1				
¾				
½				

DIAMOND GRADING REPORT

A Diamond Grading Report (*or Certificate*) is issued by the Gem Trade Laboratories and is widely used for stones of very fine quality over one carat (*but can start from 0.47ct*) Smaller diamonds are often certificated by reputable shops themselves. The purpose of the report is to confirm that the stone is genuine and to evaluate each of the important factors which affect quality, beauty, weight and thus, the value. It is also useful for insurance purposes as the information which the report contains is critical to identifying the stone.

UNDERSTANDING A DIAMOND REPORT AND HOW TO READ IT

1. Always check the date.

2. Is the Report issued by a reputable laboratory? (*see the list provided of known laboratories*).

3. Does the Report identify the type of stone? The Report should be headed 'Diamond Grading Report'. If not, it must state that the stone is a genuine diamond.

4. Shape, Weight and Dimensions
    The Report must give the description of the shape, exact carat weight and dimensions as this information is useful for insurance and identity purposes.

5. Proportion and Finish
    This information will tell you how good the 'make' of the stone is.

6. Clarity grade
    (*See the Clarity Grade chapter*) and illustration of the symbols for 'Inclusions and Blemishes'.

7. Colour Grade
    Colour is the factor, with which most people are familiar and it is very easy to understand.

8. Flourescence
    Fluorescence is the property which is possessed by some 50 per cent of all diamonds, and the characteristic of a fluorescent diamond is to emit a light blue or, rarely a light green, yellow or reddish fluorescence. This property in a stone can be seen with a long-wave ultra-violet lamp. In general, this property is of no importance and does not effect the price except in the United States where fluorescent diamonds are much sought-after and command a higher price.

SAMPLE OF GIA DIAMOND GRADING REPORT

 GIA GEM TRADE LABORATORY

A Division of GIA Enterprises, Inc.
A Wholly Owned Subsidiary of the Nonprofit Gemological Institute of America, Inc.

580 Fifth Avenue	550 South Hill Street	1630 Stewart Street
New York, New York 10036-4794	Los Angeles, California 90013-2417	Santa Monica, California 90404-4088
(212) 221-5858	(213) 629-5435	(310) 828-3148
FAX: (212) 575-3095		FAX: (310) 829-1790

10/12/94   **DIAMOND GRADING REPORT**   8507589

THE FOLLOWING WERE, AT THE TIME OF THE EXAMINATION, THE CHARACTERISTICS OF THE DIAMOND DESCRIBED HEREIN BASED UPON 10× MAGNIFICATION (FULLY CORRECTED TRIPLET LOUPE AND BINOCULAR MICROSCOPE), DIAMONDLITE AND MASTER COLOR COMPARISON DIAMONDS, ULTRAVIOLET LAMPS, MILLIMETER GAUGE, CARAT BALANCE, PROPORTIONSCOPE, AND ANCILLARY INSTRUMENTS AS NECESSARY.

RED SYMBOLS DENOTE INTERNAL CHARACTERISTICS (INCLUSIONS). GREEN SYMBOLS DENOTE EXTERNAL CHARACTERISTICS (BLEMISHES). SYMBOLS INDICATE TYPE, POSITION AND APPROXIMATE SIZE OF CHARACTERISTICS. DETAILS OF FINISH ARE NOT SHOWN. DIAGRAM MAY BE APPROXIMATE.

KEY TO SYMBOLS

CRYSTAL
NEEDLE

 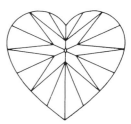

SHAPE AND CUTTING STYLE .. HEART BRILLIANT

Measurements .... 12.10 X 12.36 X 7.11 MM.

Weight .... 6.03 CARATS

PROPORTIONS ...

Depth .... 57.5 %

Table .... 62 %

Girdle .... THIN TO THICK, FACETED

Culet .... VERY SMALL

FINISH

Polish .... VERY GOOD

Symmetry ..... VERY GOOD

CLARITY GRADE .. VS1

COLOR GRADE ... E

Fluorescence ..... FAINT

COMMENTS:

PINPOINTS ARE NOT SHOWN.

ORIGIN:

GIA GEM TRADE LABORATORY

GIA Gem Trade Laboratory

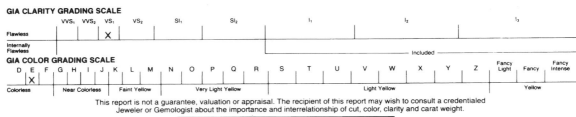

GIA CLARITY GRADING SCALE

	VVS₁	VVS₂	VS₁	VS₂	SI₁	SI₂	I₁	I₂	I₃
Flawless			X						
Internally Flawless									

Included

GIA COLOR GRADING SCALE

D	E	F	G	H	I	J	K	L	M	N	O	P	Q	R	S	T	U	V	W	X	Y	Z	Fancy Light	Fancy	Fancy Intense
	X																								
Colorless			Near Colorless				Faint Yellow				Very Light Yellow						Light Yellow								Yellow

This report is not a guarantee, valuation or appraisal. The recipient of this report may wish to consult a credentialed Jeweler or Gemologist about the importance and interrelationship of cut, color, clarity and carat weight.

Copyright © 1989 - 1994 GIA Gem Trade Laboratory

NOTICE: IMPORTANT LIMITATIONS ON REVERSE

SAMPLE OF IGI DIAMOND GRADING REPORT

INTERNATIONAL GEMMOLOGICAL INSTITUTE

SCIENTIFIC LABORATORY FOR THE IDENTIFICATION AND GRADING
OF DIAMONDS AND COLORED STONES
EDUCATIONAL PROGRAMS

Expertise issued by I.G.I. b.v.b.a.
Head Office and Laboratories.
1/7 Schupstraat, 2018 Antwerp - Belgium
Tel. (32-3) 231 68 45 (6 L.) - Fax. (32-3) 232 07 58

DIAMOND REPORT

This report is a statement of the diamond's identity and grade including all relevant information about the submitted stone.

Number: SPECIMEN

ANTWERP, 23 JUNE 1994

LABORATORY REPORT (ORIGINAL)

TO WHOM IT MAY CONCERN.

DESCRIPTION:	NATURAL DIAMOND
SHAPE AND CUT:	ROUND BRILLIANT
WEIGHT:	1.01 Carat
MEASUREMENTS:	6.51 - 6.54 x 3.91mm
PROPORTIONS and FINISH	
Table Diameter Percentage	62 %
Crown Height Percentage	13.5 %
Pavilion Depth Percentage	43 %
CULET SIZE:	POINTED
GIRDLE THICKNESS:	MEDIUM (FACETED)
FINISH : Polish-Sym/Prop	GOOD / VERY GOOD
CLARITY GRADE (10 ×):	INTERNALLY FLAWLESS
COLOR GRADE:	F(1+)
FLUORESCENCE:	VERY SLIGHT

The symbols do not usually reflect the size of the characteristics.
Red symbols indicate internal characteristics.
Green symbols indicate external characteristics.

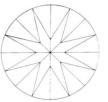

COMMENTS:

(insignificant **external** details, visible under high magnification, are not mentioned)

Control Department

LABORATORY DIRECTOR, GEMMOLOGIST

SPACE FOR DOUBLE CHECK, CLARITY AND COLOR GRADE

CLARITY GRADE:	Internally Flawless,	vvs 1	vvs 2	vs 1	vs 2	si 1	si 2	p 1	p 2	p 3	

COLOR GRADE:	0+	0	1	1	2	3	4	5	6	7	8	9	10	11	12	13	FANCY COLOR
	D	E		G	H	I	J	K	L	M	N	O	P	Q	R	20	

PROPORTIONS - MARGIN: ± 1%.
MEASUREMENTS - MARGIN: ± 0.02 mm.

The gemmological analysis of diamonds, precious stones and other minerals must be carried out by specialized gemmologists with many years' experience in this field who have a keen sense of the professional code of ethics governing their work as well as a thorough knowledge of crystallographic, optical and physical phenomenon.

The identification of the various species and varieties of stones, the distinction between natural and synthetic stones, as well as various treatment methods currently encountered are all very important factors.

More specifically for diamonds, the laws of refraction and dispersion of light, the related geometric data as well as knowledge of all aspects involved in the cutting process are essential.
Definition of a stone's color requires knowledge of type Ia, Ib, IIa and IIb diamonds, and correct use of masterstones and other relevant techniques. In order to grade the clarity of a diamond, the nature, number, size and location of any inclusions as well as any other secondary external characteristics must be determined.

This report is subject to the terms and conditions set forth on reverse.
© 1990

SAMPLE OF HRD DIAMOND GRADING REPORT

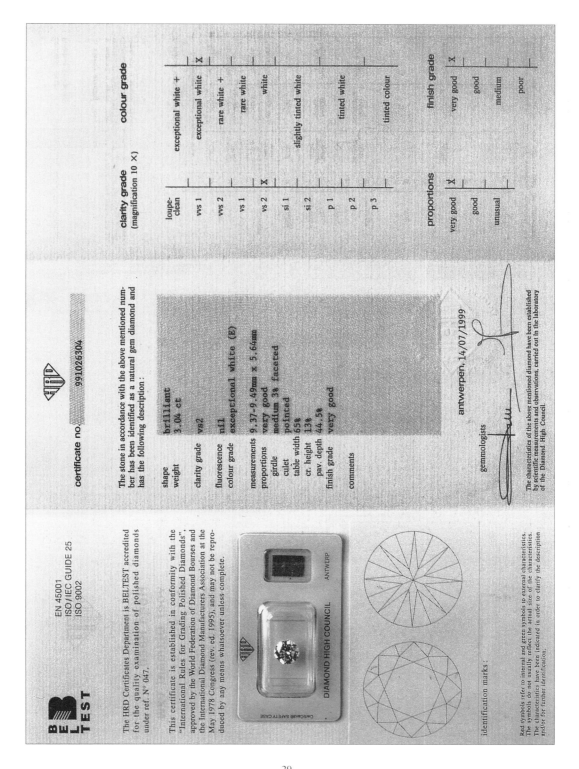

SYMBOLS FOR INCLUSIONS AND BLEMISHES

The following symbols are internationally accepted by the Gem Trade Laboratories when issuing a Diamond Grading Report. On the Report, red symbols denote internal characteristics (*inclusions*) and green symbols denote external characteristics (*blemishes*).

Symbols representing internal characteristics

pinpoint	large dark or coloured inclusion
group pinpoint	dark or coloured inclusion surrounded by a cloud
dark spot	small cleavage or crack
group of dark spots	larger cleavage or crack
cloud of tiny light pinpoints	girdle fringes
colourless crystals	girdle cleavage surrounded by a cloud
group of colourless crystals	growth of twin line, colourless
cleavages around colourless crystal	growth of coloured or black twin line

Symbols representing external characteristics

minor natural	scratch
natural with trigons	polishing lines
indented natural	indentation mark
girdle nick	growth line or twinning line
minor girdle roughness	rough culet
girdle roughness	abraded culet
girdle fringes	extra facet
group of small pits	edge damage
pit or cavity	

LASER INSCRIPTIONS

Lazare Kaplan International Inc. of New York, has patented a system for inscribing insignia, letters or numbers on the surface of a diamond using a unique laser technique. Approximately 240 characters can be laser inscribed on the girdle of a diamond, 40–80 microns high and 3 microns deep, depending on the width of the girdle and size of the gem. The procedure has been proven to be perfectly safe, as tens of thousands of stones have been lasered without a single accident.

The Gemological Institute of America Gem Trade Laboratory (GTL) has attested that the laser inscription service provided by GTL, or of an equivalent quality does not affect the clarity or the colour of a faceted diamond. The GIA GTL may grade such inscribed diamonds as flawless if they meet the grading criteria for these clarity grades. The GIA views the laser inscription as a positive rather than a negative feature of diamond identification.

The inscription, which is invisible to the naked eye, may be seen through a x10 loupe or microscope. The inscription can only be removed by repolishing on a diamond cutting wheel. This may result in weight loss and change of diameter.

For consumers, this development can reassure diamond owners that if they ever need their diamond reset, or if it is lost or stolen they will have positive proof of identification and ownership. Police departments and insurance companies now have a unique way of identifying lost or stolen gems.

NAMES OF LEADING
INTERNATIONAL GEM TRADE LABORATORIES

The Gem Testing Laboratory of Great Britain
GAGTL, 27 Greville Street, London EC1N 8TN
Telephone: 020 7405 3351 Fax: 020 7831 9479

American Gemological Laboratory
580 Fifth Avenue
New York, NY 10036

Gemmological Lab, Gubelin
Denkmalstrasse, 2
Ch-6006 Luzern, Switzerland

GIA Gem Trade Laboratory
Gemological Institute of America
580 Fifth Avenue
New York, NY 10036

IGI International Gemmological Institute
Schupstraat 1/7
2018 Antwerp, Belgium

Hoge Raad voor Diamant (HRD)
Hoveniersstraat, 22
B-2018 Antwerp, Belgium

Schweizerische Stirtung fur Edelstein-Forschung (SSEF)
Lowenstrasse, 17
Ch-8001 Zurich, Switzerland

ADL	Antwerp Diamond Laboratory
CIB	C.I.B.J.O.
CSA	Jewellery Council of South Africa
EGL	European Gemmological Laboratory (Antwerp & London)
EGI	European Gemmological Institute (Antwerp)
GII	National Gemological Institute of Israel
HRG	Heinz R. Gartner, DGemG, F.G.A. (Germany)
VPT	Verena Pagel-Theisen, DGemG, F.G.A. (Germany)
WG	Werner Galia, DGemG, (Germany)
DGL	Diamond Grading Laboratories (London)